Shell Beach

Matt Sims

High Noon Books
Novato, California

Editor: Becky Allen
Cover Illustration: Sandy Rabinowitz
Interior Illustrations: Rick Hackney

International Standard Book Number: 1-57128-246-7

Set ISBN: 1-57128-244-0
Set ISBN-13: 978-1-57128-244-6

16 15 14 13 12 11
14 13 12 11 10 09 08 07

Contents

A Trip to the Coast

The bus ride to Shell Beach was long. Rain beat on the glass by our side. We could not see past the gray haze.

At last the brakes made a screech, and the bus came to a stop.

Then Gramp drove up in his truck.

"You made it!" said Gramp as he gave us each a hug. "Not the best day to come to the beach."

You could tell that Gramp made his home by the sea. His skin was tan and thick from the sun. He had flip flops on

"You made it!" said Gramp.

his feet, and his pants were cut off.

"Just toss your bags in the back," Gramp said. "The three of us can squeeze in the cab."

As we drove, we could smell the sea air. Then we could hear the crash of waves. Rain or shine, we were glad to be by the sea.

A Day at the Beach

The sun woke us up at six. Brad and I ran to the deck to check out the beach. The sea was still and clear like a lake.

"What a switch!" said Brad. "You would

not think that was the same sea."

"We need to get down there while it is still nice out," I said. "I will tell Gramp where we will be."

We made a step on to the soft sand. Our feet sank deep as we went down the bank to the sea.

"Did you bring some thing to feed the sea gulls?" Brad said.

"Just some stale buns that Gramp gave me," I said. Then I broke off some bits and made a toss in the air. The sea gulls dove in for the prize.

Brad had a disk that he rode on the wet sand.

He would wait for a wave to rush up. Then he would toss the disk down and jump on it. At times he could glide for ten feet or so.

There was lots of fun stuff to do at Shell Beach. We could write in the wet sand and shape it in to things. We could pick up shells and

dig for crabs. But some
times it was fun just to
lie on the beach and let
the waves sweep past
us. The ice cream truck
could ring its bell. But
we would stay by the
sea and let it cast its
spell on us.

The Whale

One day Gramp got up
with the sun to get in
line at the bait shop.
Soon he came home
with a box of fresh squid
that the three of us
could share. When you
stay with Gramp, you

have to at least try to catch a fish.

Gramp gave a yell up the stairs. "You will miss the fish! Grab a rod and meet me by the bench."

Brad and I did not care if we got a fish or not. But we got our rods and went to look for Gramp.

When Gramp saw us, he gave a yell "Look down there!"

Brad and I sprang up to look down the beach. Gramp had seen a big gray mass near the sea. Brad and I ran to check it out.

"It is a whale!" we cried. "Gramp! Come see."

"It is a whale!" we cried. "Gramp, come see."

The whale lay on its side on the wet sand. Gramp bent down to feel its skin. "This whale still has some life in it," he said. "We have got to help it."

Phone for Help

"Stay here, Gramp," Brad said. "We will run home and get a pail. We can use it to keep the whale wet."

"Phone for help!" said Gramp as we ran for the pail.

When we got back home, we were in a real fix. We could not spot the phone.

"Is there a phone in the truck?" Brad said. Then he made a dash to see. But the truck had no phone.

"We do not have time for this," I said. "Take the pail to the

The truck had no phone.

beach. I will ride the bike to the home down the street."

When I got to the home, I ran up the steps and rang the bell. Soon, a man came out to greet me. He was glad to let me use his phone.

"You need to speak to Dutch," said the man. "He can help."

Home to the Sea

Dutch was a strong man the age of Gramp. He had spent his life by the sea. He had seen lots of whales get swept up on the beach.

Dutch drove his van down the dunes to the

sea. Then he and three men got a huge mat out of the back of the van.

Dutch had a plan. "We need to slide the whale on top of this mat," he said. "Then we can drag her to the sea and float her out where it is deep."

Six of us set the mat close to the whale. Then

inch by inch, we slid the
beast on top of the mat.
Three of us got on each
side to grip the mat.
Then Dutch gave a yell.

Soon the whale was
in the waves, and we
could lift her with ease.
But she tried to thrash
her tail and swim off.

"Not yet," Dutch
spoke to her. "Up here

Three of us got on each side to grip the mat.

where the sea is deep.
Now you can go!"

The whale was free!
She was off to her home
in the deep, deep sea.

The Last Day

This was the best trip we had had to Shell Beach. We were sad when it had to end. But we still had fun on our last day. We got out the sail boat and went for a spin in the bay.

Gramp kept his sail boat at a dock on the bay. The sails were like stiff sheets. I gave them a yank and up they went. The red, white, and green stripes stuck out in the clear sky.

"Press your feet on the dock and send us off," Gramp said to Brad. Soon the boat was out of the dock.

"Now the breeze will take the sails," Gramp said. The craft was soon in the bay and on its way down the coast.

With the wind in my face, I could think of just one thing. This was the life for me.

High Frequency Words

come	one	to
could	or	was
do	our	were
down	out	what
for	said	where
from	saw	who
have	some	would
her	soon	you
look	the	your
now	there	
of	they